Tones

Of The

Throne

Room

Workbook

By

Cheryl Salem

Tones of the Throne Room Workbook

ISBN 1-890370-32-0

Printed in United States of America

Copyright © 2016 by Salem Family Ministries

Salem Family Ministries

PO Box 1595

Cathedral City, CA 92234

www.salemfamilyministries.org

Disclaimer: The views expressed in this workbook contain my personal opinions and experiences throughout my life and time spent in God's presence. I express them as my opinion and view only, and share them with you from my personal lifelong experience from my heart. I am only communicating what has worked for me personally, and what I have personally experienced with the Lord.

Tones of the Throne Room Chapters

How to use this workbook

Tones Of The Throne Room Workbook is designed to be a companion prayer journal workbook to go with the Tones of the Throne Room book. As you read the chapters in Tones Of The Throne Room take the time to work the pages before the Lord in prayer and time spent with Him, searching your heart, mind, soul, and spirit to develop the highest level of worshiper the Lord has designed you to be. Within the very DNA of your cellular level you were created to worship Him! God has put the tone of His throne room within the cellular level of every human being. We love sound, respond to it, because our very DNA is tuned to the frequency of the throne room of God!

Like all things human, and on the earth, we must develop what we have been given. Use this time with your Father in the secret place of His presence to bring to the forefront of your personal worship the truth and spirit of who you are designed to be inside your Father God!

Don't hurry. Take your time. This is not a race or even a destiny. This is a journey . . . a journey of His presence to develop the core of your reason for 'being'. He will never leave you nor forsake you. Enjoy each day, each prayer, each moment in His presence as you develop the worshiper within. If He says, "Be still and don't move" then obey that still small voice of the Father God. He has a plan for you during these days. You are not required to finish X amount of pages per day to be approved. You are approved by your Father God. He adores you.

Be honest with yourself and your Lord. He deserves it and so do you. Don't 'try', just 'be'. Be still and know that I AM God! This is a promise from heaven for all of us. When you come away in the secret place of His presence you will find who you really are, and what your purpose is.

Relax. Enjoy the ride of His Spirit. You are a worshiper. You don't 'do' worship. You 'are' worship. So just be who you were created to be.

I believe you will discover the secret of the very existence of who you are within the throne room of His presence. Don't be afraid to make all kinds of sounds as He directs and instructs . . . even if the sound He demands is your silence. Give Him what He asks, and hear the worshiper from within you arise to the highest heights of His presence.

School of Worship

Purpose:

To raise up worshipers with a clean heart, called to be instruments of worship by the Holy Spirit. To define the innate difference between worshiper and musician, singer, dancer, artist, performer, etc. This School of Worship is for those who are willing to lay down their lives, to be completely His, to live and to be used by Him with humility, purity, integrity, and accountability.

This is a school of heart first, then of thought and purpose. I ask you to seek the Lord over these coming days, listen, write down what He tells you, and obey His voice. Ask the Lord to show you what He longs for you to know. Ask the Father to reveal to you His specific purpose, for you, in this great scheme of your life of worship. Ask yourself:

Where do I fit as a worshiper?

_____
_____
_____
_____

What am I already doing right?

_____
_____
_____

What do I need to change to come even closer to His throne and bow down before Him?

_____
_____
_____
_____

Worship is about the journey, the romance, with the Lord. Your concern here is not about the destination but the daily pursuit of the Lover of your soul from this day all the way into eternity. This 'road of worship' is not a sprint but rather a marathon, so pace yourself in His presence to be able to go the distance.

Worship is about the rhythm of our romance with the One who gave Himself for us. Song of Solomon 6:3, "I am my beloved's and my beloved is mine."
I may be familiar to you because we have met many times before as worshipers. Come with me today and we will worship the King together. Look for me! I will meet you at His feet! Oh, that's where I know you! I have been with you at His feet many times before but not nearly as many as we will experience into eternity! Come up higher, and I will show you . . . YOURSELF, as His highest worshiper!

Worshipers Prayer of Surrender

"Let the words of my mouth and the meditation of my heart be acceptable in Your sight, my strength and my redeemer! What can the instrument do apart from the One who is doing the playing? The instrument can do nothing, apart from the One. So, here I am Lord, play me. Make me your melody, Your lyric, Your sound! Let me be the sound through which the world hears and recognizes the very existence of an all- powerful God! Let the world hear through me the sound waves of Your love, Your overpowering strength, Your pure and cleansing streams. Lord, use me; play me as Your instrument of pleasure. Let the sound waves of your presence come forth beckoning, crying out, singing, renewing, reviving, quickening, all who long for You! Let them hear You through me. I have come before You, and I lay myself, this instrument at Your feet. Lord come down from Your holy habitation, reach down, and pick me up, into Your hands. May Your mighty anointed hands; play the sounds of healing and restoration. Play the sounds of Your glory rising and cleansing all who will listen!"

I am a woodwind instrument set before You to be played. Without the breath of Your divine presence, no sound of any value or worth can come forth. I am a stringed instrument laid at Your feet. Without Your divine fingers strumming, plucking, running over the reverberations of these yielded strings, no sound can come forth. I am any and all instruments awaiting the glorious and divine touch of Your presence. Without Your touch, I am a clanging cymbal and a sounding brass, a broken and unproductive sound wave that moves no one and goes nowhere.

Lord, I am Yours. I trust You. I will no longer belong to You part of the time, and myself part of the time. I belong to You. If there is no sound coming from me, then it is the divine Musician who wishes for this silence, not the instrument. This instrument no longer has a will, for I freely give myself, my will, my mind, my body, my instrument to my divine Creator.

May the light of your glory be seen in me. May the sound of Your presence be heard through me. I am Yours and You are mine. This is My Beloved's song, an eternal love song, but only those who are washed clean by the blood of the Lamb can hear it. Can you hear it? It is the sound of the redeemed crying loudly...even so, "Come, Lord Jesus!"
And the Bridegroom says, "I am coming quickly."
And the Bride says, "Come, Lord, Jesus."
And the Bridegroom says, "I am coming soon."
And the Bride says, "Come, Lord, Jesus."
And the Bridegroom says, "Behold! It is finished; I am coming."
And he Bride says, "Even so! Come, Lord, Jesus!

Chapter One
The Vision

Chapter One
The Vision

Did you say the worshiper's prayer aloud today? If not, then go back in the book and read it out loud. Make it your prayer to the throne room of heaven. Take ownership of each word as your own words of prayer and surrender to the One Creator who made you to worship. Surrender every area that you had held on to like a badge of honor. Give it all to Him. Give Him every pain, hurt, earthly identity, broken place, and trust Him to show you who you really are, inside of Him.

God is calling us to see what others cannot see, to hear what others choose not to hear. The realm of eternity is more real than the realm of earth. Are you willing to step into your true identity and destiny and leave this earth realm behind you to discover the truth about whom you really are? Selah, pause and calmly think about that for a moment.

Ask God to open the heavens above you and show you visions of God. Are you willing to stop everything and slow yourself down enough to really hear and see from heaven? What's stopping you?

_____
_____
_____

What are you afraid of? _____
_____
_____
_____
_____
_____

Read Ezekiel 1 aloud and let the words sink into your spirit. Now set your stopwatch on your phone and pray in tongues out loud for three minutes. Now interpret what you got from heaven through your prayer language in English. Write down what the Lord has given you.

_____
_____
_____
_____
_____
_____

God's word is powerful, like a two edged sword.   This is a Greek word. What is the word and define and explain it so you understand what happens when you put sound to God's word.

The word is _____. It is pronounced as _____.

The definition of the word is _____

_____

What happens when you say out of your mouth what God has already said in His word? _____

_____

_____

Whose mouth is always first? _____

Then whose mouth is second? _____

This puts our _____ in agreement with God's _____.

How do we know the difference between our will and God's will?

_____

_____

_____

_____

In the two visions that Ezekiel had in the Book of Ezekiel chapter 1 and John had in Revelation 4 both these prophets saw the same vision.   These visions were given at a significant amount of time between them.   They both saw the throne room of God.   In the two visions they both saw many of the exact same things. They both saw the throne, and the four living creatures, and John saw a circle of elders, encircling the outer area, and Ezekiel saw that as a wheel within a wheel. But one thing they both saw was crystal.   John saw it as a floor and Ezekiel saw it as a ceiling.   Give the two verses where each prophet describes this crystal image, and explain why one was seeing it as a floor and the other as a ceiling?

Ezekiel _____ Revelation _____

How can this be?

_____

_____

_____

_____

What two colors have represented the nation of Israel throughout the Bible?
_____

The mention of the two stones, the first and last stones on the High Priest's breastplate gives us a clear understanding of who is actually sitting on this throne in the center of the throne room.   Who is sitting there? _____

What are the two stones? _____

Read Ezekiel 28:17-19 and list the 12 stones in order as they are given.   How are they arranged on the breastplate of the High Priest?   How many rows are there? Remember in Hebrew the stones are arranged as letters written which would be right to left, the opposite of our English writing.

1. _____
2. _____
3. _____
4. _____
5. _____
6. _____
7. _____
8. _____
9. _____
10. _____
11. _____
12. _____
How many rows? _____

How many stones in each row? _____

According to Hebrews 3:1 Jesus Christ is seated on the throne and is called both the apostle and the _____ of our confession, Jesus Christ.

In Revelation 21:19 list the 12 foundational stones in the New Jerusalem.

1. _____
2. _____
3. _____
4. _____
5. _____
6. _____
7. _____
8. _____
9. _____
10. _____
11. _____
12. _____

Between the two languages of Hebrew and Greek one must decipher the names of the stones but to clarify for you these are the same 12 stones in both the High Priest's breastplate and the foundational stones of the New Jerusalem, the city of the bride of Christ. The order is arranged differently but the stones are the same.

When we take on the sound of our Bridegroom Jesus Christ and we begin to make His sound instead of our own earthly sounds, then our worship is high enough and acceptable to be heard in the throne room of heaven. The four living creatures and the twenty-four elders cry out in responsive worship to our Savior and King, Jesus Christ, forever and ever! Come on, take a moment, and join in responsive worship, antiphonal sounds of Heaven and Earth worship coming together to lift up the King of Kings!

After you have worshiped for at least five minutes then do it again in tongues! Open your Bible and sing a few Psalms to Him, then in tongues to Him, in Spirit and Truth!

Write out a four-phrase verse, then a four-phrase chorus as a private love song between you and the very Lover of your soul! He deserves your 'new song' worship. Don't judge it or be afraid. Everything you do, everything you are, He adores you! Sing, and write now!

_____

_____

_____

_____

_____

_____

_____

_____

_____

If you would like to write a 2nd verse and even a bridge go ahead; you are anointed and appointed for such a time as this!

_____

_____

_____

_____

_____

_____

_____

_____

Chapter Two
Sing a New Song

Chapter Two
Sing a New Song

Psalm 96:1, "Oh, sing to the Lord a new song! Sing to the Lord, all the earth."

King David did something no other king had done before him or after him.   He removed the veil that separated human beings from the Holy of Holies where God's presence dwelt.   What were the dimensions of the veil?

_____

What did King David use to replace the veil of separation?

_____

What position did the worshipers face?

_____

Their faces were toward _____ and their backs were toward the _____.

How is this different from our modern day worship?

_____
_____
_____

When you are worshiping the Lord what is your biggest challenge when facing the people instead of facing the altar?

_____
_____
_____
_____

When you are on the platform, or in your seat during the song portion of worship what mental exercises do you do to keep your mind on the Lord?

_____
_____
_____

Most of us are performers by nature, needing approval from people, and wanting to please people.   Do you find it difficult to sing to the Lord and not entertain the people with a song?

_____
_____

David understood better than anyone before or after him that worship was a personal and private time of intimacy with the Father God. We know this by reading and singing his writings of the Psalms. His emotions were all over the place depending on what he was going through at the moment he was writing. This is much like our own worship of intimacy with the Father. When we are truthful and honest whatever we are going through affects the tone of our worship. The Lord wants us to worship Him in spirit and truth (John 4:22-24). For us to be in 'truth' worship then we must sing the truth back to Him, which is His own word! This is responsive worship, or antiphonal worship. David mastered this within his kingdom during his reign. He removed the veil and replaced it with worshipers; twenty-four hours a day, on shifts, worshipers came in, faced the altar of the Holy of Holies, with their backs to the inner court where people were, and they sang songs directly from God's own truth. They sang the scriptures to tunes given to them by the Holy Spirit (Spirit worship). Singing the scriptures of truth led by the Holy Spirit is the ultimate of spirit and truth worship before the Lord. This antiphonal worship in response to God's own word is the epitome of singing a new song to the Lord!

Stop for a moment and open your Bible to the Psalms. Choose one, any particular Psalm that is your favorite. Close your eyes and come into the secret place with the Lord. Shut the door on distractions of your mind, and even on natural distractions. (Matthew 6:6) Let's go together; close your eyes and come into the throne room with the Lord. Can you see Him seated on the throne? He is our great High Priest. The throne room is circular, so look around in a circle in your mind. Begin to shut all the doors of distractions in your life. Shut the door on those immediate things that want to pull your attention away; lay down those things that simply must get done today; lay down the nagging sound of the washer/dryer calling your name to turn over the next load of laundry. Shut it all down for a moment. If you have to, go into a room, and shut the actual door. Slowly turn in a circle in your mind and close everything and anything, even all the people who pull on your attention. Now all the doors are shut. You are in the secret place with the One who adores you, who loves you more than you can ever imagine.

Open your eyes, and find your favorite Psalm. Now open your mouth and allow sound to come forth. Don't worry about the tune, or your sound. Your tone is exactly what the Father has been waiting and longing for so long! Sing His own words back to the throne room of the Lord. You are the TONE OF THE THRONE ROOM right now. It's your sound of worship He has longed to hear. Sing the entire Psalm to Him. He loves your sound. Don't disqualify the tone, and frequency of your voice that He has placed within your divine instrument. You are not the judge; you are simply the instrument. SING! SING A NEW SONG!

Now write how you feel at this moment. Write your deepest thoughts that are coming forth by His spirit leading you from within. Write your heart to His heart. Don't hold back, or halter, or judge. Just write. Write the deepest of love songs, love poems to the One who loves you!

_____
_____
_____
_____
_____
_____
_____
_____
_____
_____

If you have not read and worked the workbooks on **We Who Worship** and **Rebuilding the Ruins of Worship** I encourage you to do so! This is the third book and workbook in a series about worship. You are here now so don't stop; keep going, but I anticipate after you finish this one that you will want to go back and begin at the beginning of this journey with me.

The simplest of changes like turning the worshipers toward the altar with their backs to the 'audience' could completely change the atmosphere of worship. It could remove the spirits of _____. _____, and _____. These spirits have taken the attention away from the throne room of God, and turned our thoughts as worshipers inward to ourselves. This makes us more 'self aware' instead of God aware while worshiping, and literally causes what should have been worship to be nothing more than singing a 'gig' or 'set' or whatever else word musicians want to put on a list of songs that should have been there as a guide. These songs we practice should be practiced to the highest levels of excellence so we are able to give back to the Lord, then before the service begins, should be laid at His feet for His will, His purpose and plan to come forth. Whether we sing all, or none of what we have rehearsed is none of our concern as long as the Spirit of God is leading and has control of what we term the 'worship service'.

To sing a new song is not a request but a command from heaven. Who is this command directed toward?

_____

What should you be doing right now?

_____

Familiar songs that we have memorized come out of what side of our brain memory?

_____

Singing a new song from our creative spirit man then must come forth from which side of our brain?

_____

Singing new songs causes us to be more like our _____ and since we are made in His image He must be very pleased when He sees and hears Himself coming forth from His creation.   Like all parents we want to find something, even an ear lobe, or a crooked smile in our infants that reminds us of ourselves.   So does our Father God! He longs to see Himself in us! He made us in His image, His creative-power filled image!

Are all 'new songs' using the words of the scriptures? Can there be other types of 'new songs'?   If so, then explain.

_____
_____
_____
_____

Romans 8:26 gives a descriptive explanation of a song without any words at all, just sounds coming forth. Who makes these sounds within our vocal instrument?

_____

At some point after King David, another king put the huge thick fabric veil back up between the Holy of Holies and the inner court.   We know this because when Jesus was crucified and His work as the sacrificial Lamb was completed He cried out, "It is finished."   Just as His sound came forth from the cross on Calvary, across Jerusalem within the temple, Caiaphas, the high priest was making preparations to go behind the veil to offer the yearly sacrifice for the Jewish people.   Can you imagine as he stood there just outside the veil, Jesus having cried out with a loud voice, using His human instrument of sound and frequency waves, to proclaim that the last and ultimate sacrifice had been given, that all mankind's debt has been paid, that veil begins to rip sixty feet in the air, from the very top, smack dab in the middle of it!   The rip must have been extremely loud, and this heavy, very thick, veil was ripped from the sound of Jesus' voice, from sixty feet in the air from top to the very bottom! It fell in two huge pieces at the feet of Caiaphas, the high priest, and the Holy of Holies, the very presence of God was exposed for all mankind to have access to God's presence.

What caused this veil to rip from sixty feet in the air, downward all the way to the ground?

_____

When I stand in God's presence I don't plead guilty, even though I am; I don't plead innocent for that would be a lie; I _____.

When we turn our backs to the people in worship this very act causes us to become _____.

Worship is _____ and intercession is _____.

The sound of worship should never cease at the altar of God. David managed to get the worshipers to understand that they were the veil that protected the people in the inner court from the very presence of the fire of God within the Holy of Holies. This meant that the worshipers stood facing the altar with their _____ touching one another. This also meant that the sound coming forth from the worshipers never stopped. There was never a moment of silence. The worshipers were so well trained that while one worshiper was finishing up a scripture the next worshiper was already making sound! The coverage was not only their physical sanctified, holy bodies, but also their sanctified, holy SOUND! Worshipers must understand the requirements for position within the throne room is purified by the fire of God's presence, holy, acceptable, priesthood life style.

Examine your own life for a moment and make a list below of those things you need to lay down at His feet to live to the highest levels required to truly be a worshiper in His presence.   Don't forget thoughts and mental areas of 'lack of submission.' Much of our holy lives must start in our thinking. Usually our actions start with un-repented mentality. Ask the Holy Spirit to show you the last and deepest levels you need to lay at His feet. He will show you! He knows us better than we know ourselves!

_____
_____
_____
_____
_____
_____
_____
_____
_____
_____
_____

Worship is not a competition. Worship is an _____ and a _____.
It doesn't matter what sound you make as long as you make it for His _____.
He made you for giving _____. He longs for you to worship Him!
Your sound is for His glory not your _____, so get over yourself and worship!

In a vision the Lord spoke directly to me and said, "You are My woodwind instrument. Unless I pick you up, and put My mouth on you, unless I blow My Spirit breath through you there is no sound coming forth from you that is worthy for Me to hear. I will play you for My glory.   I will blow forth My breath through you; I will cause the highest worship to come forth from your being to My throne room. In this I am well pleased."

What do you hear the Father saying to you from this heaven to earth vision for worshipers? Worship is not nor has it ever been about gifting or talent. We have made it about that but the Father never has done that. Therefore, I realized that up until that moment when I heard from heaven that nothing I had ever given to Him before in what I termed worship was really and truly the kind of worship He deserved. I changed. I turned around and faced Him. I stopped comparing my sound to others, and I stopped talking badly about my instrument. I celebrate who I am and the sound that I make for His glory. What can you do to be a more acceptable sacrifice of worship before Him?

_____
_____
_____
_____
_____
_____

Don't continue to be satisfied with your last encounter with the Most High God! Come up higher in His presence when you worship and allow His sound to become your sound.   The Spirit of God says, (write what He says to you!)
"
_____
_____
_____.

Why do many pastors have to shut down 'Spirit led worship' during Sunday morning multiple services?

_____
_____
_____
_____

As worshipers we must remember to be subject and stay submitted to our leadership and the lead pastor wherever we are. We must keep our spirits within the throne room of God and a portion of our brain on the clock and be obedient to the time constraints of multiple services, children's workers, volunteers, etc.

One of our biggest mental mistakes in flowing in the Spirit during a service is we wait for a 'feeling' that the Spirit of God is with us. Then once we finally get ourselves within the very presence of God we don't want to leave. We 'wait' for the Spirit of God to 'lift' and remove Himself. Why is this wrong thinking?

_____

_____

_____

_____

Jehovah Shammah means _____.

So understanding Who God is explains that He never leaves us nor forsakes us. He is EVER WITH US, EVER PRESENT. It is up to us to be obedient to the time and space constraints of earth's existence.

WE cannot 'go to the next level'; we must _____.

Sustaining and maintaining spiritual levels takes growth and _____.

Worship is not a competition or a race. Worship is intimacy; the very Lover of your souls is with you, teaching and training you the sounds and rhythms of His presence. Don't get in a hurry; don't get frustrated, or feel like you are being left behind. It's impossible to be left behind when you are walking in rhythm and step with Him!

We can never worship at a higher level publicly and corporately until we learn to worship higher privately and intimately. What can help you do this?

_____

_____

_____

_____

_____

_____

_____

_____

Use the time you are given within a service as a worshiper wisely. Don't come to corporate worship unprepared. Be ready; know the words, and the songs that have been assigned. Know the transitions and the requirements of you, but most importantly, be prayed up in advance. Start on time, quit on time. Don't be late to fulfill your requirement. Your time is not more valuable than everyone else's. Don't be late for rehearsal and don't be late for service! Don't waste everyone's time chitchatting and 'visiting' with the other worshipers. There is a time for that but rehearsals and services is not the time! Be in the spirit before you get to the building. Pray in the Holy Spirit. Read and study your Bible. Go into the secret place with the Lord daily and be ready for His presence. These disciplines will help the pastor trust you more with the time you have been given during each service. Be a good steward of your time. Jesus is coming. Don't waste a minute with idle talk. Be a good leader and give the team a solid person to follow. Give quick and easy directions to follow. Be prepared. Be prepared. Be prepared.

From the above paragraph list some of the things that jump out at you the most of what you need to do better.

_____

_____

_____

_____

_____

_____

_____

_____

_____

_____

_____

_____

As you pray and seek the Holy Spirit to guide and direct you now, what are some other things that you personally can do to be more ready to worship the King?

_____

_____

_____

_____

_____

_____

_____

_____

_____

_____

Chapter Three
Keys of the Kingdom

Chapter Three
Keys of the Kingdom

Matthew 16:19, "And I will give you the keys of the kingdom of heaven . . . "

English is my first language. Speaking in tongues is my second language. The older I get Speaking in tongues is becoming my first language! Music is my third language. Music is a language. It has it's own set of rules, and sounds, and terms. Many musicians play by ear. I play by ear. That's how I started playing the piano when I was five years old. Someone gave our family a very old very large upright piano. We lived in a four-room house way out in the country in Choctaw County, MS. I have asked the Lord many times to bless abundantly the person who gave us that old piano, because it changed my life forever.

I remember the day as if it just happened yesterday. There was a porch on that old house, a front door, and as you crossed the threshold of that door, you were standing in the living room. To the left of that room was a bedroom that my sister and I shared. Right behind the living room was my parent's bedroom. And to the left of that bedroom was the kitchen. There was no hallway or anything else. That was it. I don't have a lot of vivid memories of living there but the day that piano was rolled over the front door I have detailed memories of that moment.

It had a lot of scrollwork, detailed woodwork on it, and it had a round wooden bench that would go higher or lower just by spinning it around. It had glass balls in the four claw-like feet. As it came to a stand still and the men set it against the middle wall of that tiny room, I remember immediately turning that bench up as high as I could get it to go, climbed up on it, and put my left hand and right hand on the keys. I did not hunt or peck or search for the notes. I started playing, **'When The Saints Go Marching In.'** I played the melody with my left hand and the chords in accompaniment in the right hand. (I was born left handed, until my Mama strengthened my right hand. This made me an excellent musician as both my left and right hemispheres of my brain are equally strong!)

Playing by ear is a wonderful gift and as I grew and matured in my life and my music it was discovered that I have perfect pitch. I know what tones are just by hearing them. I know what key the song is in without having to be told. It's a gift from the Lord. The statistics are one in a million people have this gift. I am very thankful. I have told you this story so you will understand what and why I am about to make this statement.

NO MATTER HOW GIFTED AND TALENTED YOU ARE, NO MATTER HOW WELL YOU CAN PLAY AN INSTRUMENT OR SING BY USING YOUR EAR, LEARN TO READ MUSIC! Music is a language, and if you plan on being able to communicate with other musicians you need to learn to read and write in the language of trained musicians.

There are several levels of music training. Nashville musicians have made up their own language of reading and writing music as many of the studio musicians play by ear instead of learning the music language when they were young. This works in Nashville, but around the world, you are out of luck. Many people who start learning to read music in their adult lives learn to read chord charts. This is a good start and definitely much better than nothing! But to better understand music and the language of music, one must start at the beginning and learn to read and write the language of music, including the 'why' of music, called music theory. Just start. Don't say, 'It's too late; I'm too old." Old is a relative term. If you look around you can always find someone older and younger than you are right now. Don't think about your age. Think about what God is calling you to do. To worship effectively one must learn to communicate with other worshipers, SO LEARN THE LANGUAGE OF COMMUNICATING MUSIC.

Music crosses language barriers, age and generation barriers, cultural barriers, and socio-economic barriers. Music is the universal language. Use it, learn it, speak it, write it, sing it, play it!

The word of God is sharper than any two-edged sword. (Hebrews 4:12). Look up every scripture given in this workbook and read it aloud from your own Bible. Underline it in your Bible. Meditate on these scriptures throughout the day. Both music and the word of God incorporated together can bring about a 'shift' in the atmosphere of the spirit and take an entire corporate body of worshipers to the higher levels possible in any given moment!

All my workbooks are intended to go side by side with the book. So first read chapter three in Tones of the Throne Room book, and then read chapter three in the workbook. This will make the 'work' of the workbook be much smoother and more understandable for you. We are about to embark on deep territory and I want you to understand as much as possible before I 'throw you into the deep end' of God's river of life.

Jesus said in Matthew 16:19 that He will give us the keys of the kingdom. All my life when I read this scripture I thought about a literal key, like a car key or a house key. I'm laughing a little right now because car keys now don't look like 'keys' that we grew up having to the car. Ok, so think about a house key. I thought when Jesus said 'I will give you the keys,' I visualized an actual key that would open a lock of some sort. But I was totally missing what Jesus was saying and how God set up the earth and it's power.

God created the entire world that we know and call earth with sound. His sound, His words were the creative force that made everything that we call 'real' or physical, matter, etc. God made all that we know with His sound waves. God said, then God saw what He said, then God blessed what He saw that He said.

Proverbs 28:21 states that 'death and life are in the power of the tongue'. Power of death and power of life is in our own sound waves. God made us in His image (Genesis 1:26) and gave us the creative force to use here on the earth to create, to make, to subdue, to conquer, to control the earth . . . using sound, words, sound waves!

I read the Bible and pray in the spirit at the same time. I want you to do this right now. Open your Bible and read passages of scripture. Start with Matthew 16:19, then flip over to Genesis 1:26, then to Proverbs 18:21 and while you read these passages keep praying aloud in tongues. The Spirit of God will reveal more of the reality of the word of God to you while you tap into the Holy Spirit by activating your prayer language. Now stop and listen.

Write what you received in your spirit.

_____

_____

_____

_____

_____

_____

If I were going to my car, I would go to the drawer and grab the keys to the car. I would hold the keys to the car in my hand as I walked to the door of the car. Notice the preposition used each time, the keys TO the car. Now compare that preposition to the one the Holy Spirit highlighted as I prayed in the spirit and read the word in Matthew 16:19. Jesus said that He would give us the keys OF the kingdom.

When referring to a key that unlocks anything we use the preposition 'to'. But Jesus plainly said 'of the kingdom' not 'to the kingdom.' As I meditated on this simple phrase I realized the only time you use the preposition 'of' in relationship to the word keys is when giving instructions in music to others. For example, when on a worship team, or playing in a group or a band, one would say, "Let's play that song in the 'KEY OF' A." Depending on if it needs to be higher or lower one would choose one of seven different keys.

There are only seven keys in the music language. A-B-C-D-E-F-G, and if you wanted the half steps between there would be five more choices but those choices do not vary from these seven named keys. They are either a half step higher or a half step lower depending on the direction you are going. If you are going upward then you 'sharp' the note. If you are going downward, then you 'flat' the note. For example, the twelve different tones in a musical 'scale' going upward are A-A#-B-C-C#-D-D#-E-F-F#-G-G#. Twelve moves upward will complete the musical sound circle. But notice when you name the actual letters of the keys there are still only seven named keys, and five variations of those named keys.

If you are moving downward in the musical spiral staircase circle you would name the tones as A-Ab-G-Gb-F-E-Eb-D-Db-C-B-Bb, which brings us all the way back down the circle to completion, one octave lower than when we began. Twelve moves bring us once again full circle back to the lettered tone from where we started.

If you don't know the musical language don't get frustrated and quit at this point. Don't lay the book down and say I just don't understand. PRAY AND SEEK THE LORD. Allow the Spirit of God to teach and train you while you read and learn and listen and pray. You are a worshiper of the Most High God; you need to understand the depths of the language used to translate to the world.

Notice the numbers mentioned above. 7, God's perfection number of completion, the 'it is finished' number of God's numerical system. 5, God's number for grace, particularly, the number for grace in relationship to the earth. And finally, 12, God's completed number for divine governmental authority establishing His kingdom upon the earth through worship for all mankind. Music and numbers always go hand in hand. What do you hear when you study certain numbers?

_____

_____

_____

_____

_____

_____

This is the most important revelation for you to understand before we dive deeper into the mystery of the Tones of the Throne Room that concern you.   Read it over and over again until you have a 'spirit' grasp on this.   Sing aloud what you know. No matter what key (letter you start on) in music that first position is termed 'Do'. So no matter what key the music is being played in, the first position is 'Do'. The second position is 'Re'. The third position is 'Mi', so on and so forth until you make 7 moves and come back around to 'Do', a full octave higher, assuming you were ascending the scale and not descending it!

I sounds like e, e sounds like a, a sounds like ah, o sounds like long o.   Use this phonetically when you sing.   You should know the pronunciation simply from the movie, **The Sound of Music**.

Now sing aloud. Do-Re-Mi-Fa-Sol-La-Ti-Do.   Eight sounds, a full octave, as you have repeated the first tone again at a higher frequency.   Now descend singing Do-Ti-La-Sol-Fa-Mi-Re-Do.   No matter what tone you begin on, you can sing this scale in any key. Musical keys are simple.

Name the seven keys of the musical language beginning on A.
1. _____
2. _____
3. _____
4. _____
5. _____
6. _____
7. _____

Now name the twelve keys ascending the scale, naming the half steps as well as the whole steps beginning on A.
1. _____
2. _____
3. _____
4. _____
5. _____
6. _____
7. _____
8. _____
9. _____
10. _____
11. _____
12. _____

Repeat the twelve keys descending the scale, beginning on A.

1. _____
2. _____
3. _____
4. _____
5. _____
6. _____
7. _____
8. _____
9. _____
10. _____
11. _____
12. _____

I could have asked you to begin on any note and you should have been able to list the twelve moves upward or downward. Music is a concrete science and language, much like mathematics. There are no variables, only misunderstandings. Music is an exact science. Much like God, music never changes. The language of music brings peace, harmony, and unity. It was never intended to bring chaos or confusion. Only when it is misused does this happen. When used properly to create all the aspects of the fruit of the Spirit through our sound waves, God allows us to be as creative through our music as He was on the first day of earth's existence. Sound is creative. It is up to us whether it is blessing creative, or cursing creative. Sound creates regardless of motive, heart, circumstance, or situation.

When Jesus gave us the keys 'of the kingdom' it was for creative purposes here on the earth, to call forth the realm of heaven to the earth through our words, our sounds, our worship. The keys of the kingdom were to establish 'upon this rock I will build My church, and the gates of hell shall not prevail against it.' Through our worship using sound we can create such a strong barrier that the enemy cannot get to us, the church. We must understand the rock that Jesus was talking about was a revelation that Peter had just declared out of his mouth using sound. Jesus asked Peter, "Who do you say that I am?" And Peter made a declaration. What did he say?

_____

Upon the rock of the word spoken of who I AM, Jesus declared that He would build His church upon the testimony and declaration of the truth of His identity. That truth put into sound would create such a strong barrier that the enemy and all the gates of hell could not prevail against it! This should give you great confidence in the sounds you are making in worship to establish, decree, make strong, a great defense against all enemies of God's church.

So with all this above explanation plus what is written in the Tones book, when Jesus said I will give you the keys of the kingdom what was He referring?

_____

What can be bound or loosed on this earth is done so through what?

_____

In the beginning when God created the world where was Jesus at that time?

_____

Write out the scripture that proves this truth.

_____
_____
_____
_____
_____
_____

Just as who we are in triune being goes everywhere at all times, for example, when I go to the mall, I don't leave my spirit or my soul at home, all three of my beings, spirit, soul, and body go everywhere with me at all times. God who is triune, Father, Son, and Holy Ghost were at all times together for everything from before what we term beginning and past what we term the end. God who is infinite in all directions, 360 degrees at all times, God is triune, Father, Son, and Holy Spirit. So the Spirit of God was not created in Acts 2, nor was Jesus created in chapters one of the four gospels. From what we term beginning God was all in all, triune, Father, Son, and Holy Spirit. Try to wrap your finite mind around that for a moment. Now stop and worship Him, all three of Him! Write out your worship; don't judge it, just write it down. Make a verse of at least four lines and a chorus of at least four lines. Take out your phone and record the tune, as you will quickly forget with your mind what was given to your spirit.

_____
_____
_____
_____
_____
_____
_____
_____
_____
_____
_____

Now add a bridge; tell Him who He is to you every day!

_____

_____

_____

_____

_____

_____

Your songs are 'tones of the throne room' coming forth through your instrument. As you pray, study, and open your spirit up to be poured through, songs will come forth by the spirit of God. These are not songs that are filtered through your mind, or brain. These are pure, holy, perfect worship for the King! He deserves it! So go back and sing it again! Make it loud, and clear, and plain. Write more as He gives it to you. Don't be afraid. What can man do to you? This is not for man; this is for the One who made you, who created you with His sound. He put a sound wave literally in the very core of every cell within your body. Use those sounds that He put inside you to give back to Him your own personalized creative worship.

God is light. The earth is created by, from, and through sound waves. How did the Father get Jesus, who is eternal and infinite, into the earthly finite womb of young Mary?

_____

_____

_____

_____

_____

_____

According to Romans 8:1 we are not to walk in the _____ but we are to walk in the _____.

What brings the blessing of God in our lives according to Psalm 34:8?

_____

As a prophet, when Elisha was asked by the king to prophesy for him, what did Elisha ask for to motivate and inspire the prophetic gift within him?

_____

Music and the sound of music has a way of bypassing our earthly feelings and desires and can bring us into the realm of who we were created to be from the very beginning of our existence. Have you discovered that you like certain sounds, tones, and pitches better than others yet?

If so, explain.

_____
_____
_____
_____
_____

How does glass break using sound?

_____
_____
_____
_____
_____

As a worship leader should you always choose the keys for the songs that you like to sing in or are their other variables that should be considered?
Explain please.

_____
_____
_____
_____
_____

What other things should you consider when choosing songs for corporate worship?

_____
_____
_____
_____
_____

Sound and media people are a huge part of the worship team in our society today. How should they be trained when learning and teaching the entire team to flow in spirit songs to incorporate the entire congregation of worshipers?

_____
_____
_____
_____
_____

There are two directions of prophetic worship. I use the terms 'prophetic worship' and 'prophetic songs' to distinguish between the two types of worship. A prophetic song is easy to distinguish because of voicing. When the words coming forth say phrases like, "I am the Lord. You are mine. I love you, My daughter, My son." These phrases are key to knowing the Lord to singing to His people. This is a prophetic song coming from the throne room to encourage, edify, and love on God's people. When we receive a song like this during a service, we can train the media and sound people to start typing these words into the computer and then reverse the direction of the words. This will bring the entire congregation into the worship, thus turning a prophetic song into prophetic worship back to the throne room of God, giving Him His own words to us back to Him through us!
We can then sing back to Him,
"You are the Lord. We are yours and You are mine. We love you, our Father!"

Right now open your heart and mind to the Lord and allow Him to sing to you and through you a prophetic song. Write it down.

_____
_____
_____
_____
_____
_____
_____
_____
_____

Now reverse it and make it prophetic worship back to Him! Write it down.

_____
_____
_____
_____
_____
_____
_____
_____
_____

In Revelation 4:1-11 we see how many Spirits of God before the throne of our High Priest Jesus Christ?

_____

Get your Bible and turn to this chapter. Read aloud first then start again, and sing a slow beautiful melody the Lord gives you for each verse. This is the highest of worship, antiphonal worship. This is singing His own word back to the throne room. This is what David did as king. He trained 288 master musicians to sing the scriptures back to the altar of God. Those 288 master musicians kept 4000 less trained musicians on a constant relay system of sound and space. Their shoulders were always touching and their voices were always singing God's word back to His presence. They were pure, holy, reverent, and righteous. They understood the power of God and the respect it took to stand in that position. There was no 'visiting, or talking, or laughing or anything else' in that position during that time. There was a holy fear of God that is lacking and completely missing in the throne room of God in our society of so called worshipers. The power and presence of God comes with pure and holy and reverent worshipers. If we take our place, He will take His place.

Now turn to Revelation 4 and sing God's word back to Him please. He deserves it and you will love it! After you have finished singing to Him write down your thoughts.

_____
_____
_____
_____
_____
_____
_____
_____
_____
_____
_____
_____
_____
_____
_____
_____
_____
_____
_____

Chapter Four
The Seven Spirits of God

Chapter Four
The Seven Spirits of God

Revelation 4:5, " . . . Seven lamps of fire were burning before the throne, which are the seven Spirits of God."

How many Spirits of God are there?

_____

How many musical tones are there to complete a musical circle?

_____

If you begin with the named frequency 'A' name the seven pitches ascending.

_____

If you begin with 'Do' name the seven tones ascending.

_____

You may be saying that you don't understand any of this, but remember that the language of music is concrete, solid, always the same, like mathematics. Even if you don't understand how a problem is solved in math, if you apply the principle and the formula you can get the correct answer. The same applies to music. The more you write it, say it, and study it, the more you understand that music is not varied. Music is a language; it has rules and principles that work when you apply them.

Seven in God's numbers means _____.

Since there are seven Spirits of God mentioned in the above scripture and there are seven lamps of fire in correlation to the Spirits of God explain how you feel this ties in with your personal and private worship at the throne of God.

_____

_____

_____

_____

In Revelation 1:18 Jesus makes another reference to keys. Again He uses the preposition 'of' instead of 'to.' Jesus said that He is alive forevermore. This should give us great comfort knowing that we do not serve a God who is subject to death, but rather that death is subject to Him! He confirms this when He states that He has the _____.

Having taken the keys of death and hell means that Jesus literally has the frequencies, the sounds of death and the sounds of hell in His possession. This means that Satan cannot use these sounds anymore, ever again against us!

How then, do these sounds continue to be sounded within the realm of the earth if Jesus took these two sounds after the cross?

_____

_____

_____

_____

_____

According to Ezekiel 28 Lucifer, as the head worshiper, was filled with what?

_____

_____

He was covered with what?

_____

_____

Why did Lucifer rebel against God?   What did he want that he did not already have?

_____

_____

_____

_____

How many angels did Lucifer have influence over before and during the fall?

_____

_____

Give the scripture reference and write it out to prove this.

_____

_____

_____

_____

_____

What did Lucifer use to convince the angels to turn against God?

_____

_____

_____

Within this chapter there are two more references in the Book of Revelation to the number seven.   Give those two references and explain how they divinely connect to your personal and private daily worship.

_____
_____
_____
_____
_____
_____
_____
_____
_____
_____

By understanding that the seven stars are the seven angels who watch over and are assigned to the seven churches, and the seven lampstands are the seven defined and different churches on the earth at the time of the coming of the Lord, we can see how heaven divinely intersects earth, how heaven's sound and earth's sound divinely connect to form the sign of the cross!

Explain how important it is for you to keep your 'sound' in check and not make the wrong sounds, the wrong words spoken, the wrong kind of worship centered in pride rather than centered on Him and His throne.

_____
_____
_____
_____
_____

John 4:23-24 gives us a clear depiction of whom the Lord is seeking in worship. What qualifies your worship to be 'found by the Father God'?

_____
_____
_____
_____
_____

To worship Him in spirit and truth could mean that we should strive to reach a place of _____
_____
_____

Chapter Five
The Language of Worship
Through Music

Chapter Five
The Language of Worship Through Music

The seven tones in the musical scale just like the seven days of a week represent a full _____.   Each time we go through the seven positions we always come back around to start again at a higher or a lower level depending on whether we are _____ or _____ with the tones and frequencies.   The higher tones move slower or faster? _____.
The lower tones move slower or faster? _____.

The reason Do-Re-Mi is a much better way of describing the seven tones instead of the letters is _____.
If I begin a scale of seven tones in the key of C then the first and subsequent seven tones are _____.
No matter what tone (lettered sound) you begin on, once seven tones are completed it always brings you back to _____.

Since this is not a book to teach music but you must understand a small foundation of the language of music to grasp the revelation contained within this book, I want you to understand that no matter what 'key' a scale begins on, whether A, or B, or C, or D, or E, or F, or G . . . no matter which note we begin on, that first tone is called _____ and the tones that follow to complete the circle are

_____.

The musical language has a rule or law within it called the Circle of fifths. It is a rule that states no matter what note you begin, once you move 12 times on the interval of a fifth you always come full circle back to the same lettered tone you began.   A fifth is a 'Do to Sol' interval of sound.   No matter what note you begin, moving either upward or downward 12 different times using the measurement of a fifth interval of tone always brings you back to the same key on which you began.
The sounds of intervals can be remembered many times by association of familiar songs.   For example one of the easier to intervals to hear and remember can be compared to the first interval sounds in the all too familiar song, "Hear Comes The Bride".   That is the tone of a fourth interval, a Do to Fa, sound.   The Do to Mi to Sol sound, is measured in two moves of a third interval in the very old hymn, Holy, Holy, Holy, Lord God almighty.   The first 'holy' is on the 'Do', the second 'holy' is on the 'Mi', and the third 'holy, is on the 'Sol' tone.

Seven in the Hebrew language is defined as _____.
Three in the Hebrew language is defined as _____.
Five in the Hebrew language is defined as _____.
Twelve in Hebrew language is defined as _____.

The twelve movements in the circle of fifths rule in music gives us a clear picture that God and His plan for mankind and the earth is a divine plan to bring His government to the earth through our worship.   I will explain this in detail in my next book, entitled *I Am A Worshiper.*

In Luke 11:2, Jesus taught His disciples how to pray.   Write out what He instructed them to do to pray effectively.

_____

_____

_____

_____

_____

_____

_____

When you pray, _____! Making sound is very important to the realm of heaven _____.

He was teaching His disciples how to call the will of heaven to the earth. He was using sound to teach them how to use their own vocal sounds of creative power on the earth! We must do the same. Take a moment now and call heaven to earth; call the will of God to the earth through your worship sounds of prayer and intercession. Write it out as the Holy Spirit gives you the words to say!

_____

_____

_____

_____

_____

_____

_____

_____

_____

Don't be _____ when God is calling you to worship at a higher level.

Write out the verse in Esther 4:14.

_____

_____

_____

_____

_____

What is the phrase that as a worshiper and intercessor you should be focused?

_____

If I don't do my part to make my voice heard in this nation what will God do?

_____

If you disobey God when He urges you to pray, or worship, or make intercession and you remain silent, then what happens to you and your family because of your disobedience?

_____

_____

The keys of the kingdom of heaven are within you.   What sounds, words, prayers, worship, and intercession is the Holy Spirit quickening within you right now? Write it out and then say it aloud, and say it loudly so every demon in hell can hear you make proclamations, declarations, and decrees for the kingdom of God, for you and your family, and for this nation!

_____

_____

_____

_____

_____

_____

_____

_____

In Psalm 47 God commands us to make sound in two more ways.
   1. _____
   2. _____

I will add to that to dance with all your might and make sound with your feet, your clothes swishing around and any other way you can find to make the sound of worship warfare!   Ok, so stop for a minute, get out of your seat, and clap, shout, and dance for a few moments!   It's liberating for you and yes, even for others many times who are watching you!   Go ahead; be a fool for Christ!   It's an honor to lose your natural identity to find who you really are eternally!

Write how you feel after a little time of 'getting over yourself'!

_____

_____

_____

_____

Romans 9:10 and Romans 10:17 give great instructions of making sound work for our benefit while here on this earth.
Write these two scriptures out.

_____
_____
_____
_____

_____
_____
_____
_____

Hearing is a corresponding action to _____.

We need to follow these three steps daily to be whom God has called and created us to be!
1. _____
2. _____
3. _____

Faith comes when you _____ the word of God _____. _____, and _____. The _____ of God builds your faith!

What sounds have you allowed your ears to hear that have destroyed your faith? List them and as you do so, repent and ask the Lord to forgive you. Then turn from this behavior and never allow those sounds near you or your family again!

_____
_____
_____
_____
_____

Now list what sounds you are going to incorporate into your daily routine for you and your family. Don't be concerned about how you are going to do it, just list them by faith and ask the Holy Spirit to help you!

_____
_____
_____
_____
_____

Chapter Six
Two Visions

Chapter Six
Two Visions

Get your Bible and turn to the book of Ezekiel.   Now hold your place in chapter one and flip over to Revelation chapter 4.   In the book of Ezekiel we are shown through descriptive words a vision from heaven to earth that Ezekiel witnessed beginning in chapter one.   This same vision with slightly differing details was described again in the book of Revelation by John in chapter 4.   What makes the visions vary in detailed descriptions?

_____

_____

_____

In Ezekiel 1:22 we see a sea of crystal described as a _____.
In Revelation 4:6 we see a sea of crystal described as a _____.
The two different positions can be explained because Ezekiel was seeing from _____ and John was seeing from _____.
Ezekiel was looking _____ while John was looking _____.   Depending on where you are looking from, a situation or circumstance can be a much different picture for you.

In the story of Chuck Yeager breaking the sound barrier that I described in detail in the **Tones of the Throne Room** book, what is the speed that can break sound?

_____

Many died trying to break the sound barrier in the 1940's and many believed that it was an invisible unbreakable very real barrier.   The speed of any plane as it reached the approximate speed of Mach 1 could cause the plane to

_____ . _____

_____ .

What would happen when shock waves increased?

_____

_____

_____

The build up of air pressure on the front of the aircraft would cause _____ .
Because the air on top of the wing was traveling faster than the air underneath the wing it would normally cause the plane to _____ .
Some planes actually self destructed before 770 miles per hour (Mach 1) could be reached.   What nation finally broke the sound barrier? _____

Why do you believe Chuck Yeager was able to do what no other pilot before him was capable of doing? I'm asking for your opinion.

_____

_____

_____

What was the date the sound barrier was broken? _____

From where did the plane take off? _____

What kind of plane was it? _____

At what altitude did the experimental plane drop from the belly of the bomber?

_____

Two day before this forever earth-changing event what happened to Chuck?

_____

Why, in your opinion, do you believe Chuck did not quit because of the pain?

_____

_____

When Chuck Yeager broke the sound barrier what happened in your own words?
What was in the front of the plane and where did it go?   What then?

_____

_____

_____

_____

Before the sound barrier was broken what was the volume in the plane? _____
What happened once the sound barrier was broken and a sonic boom occurred?
What did Chuck hear and what did he see?

_____

_____

_____

_____

In almost every life-changing event something happens right before that causes most people to quit.   Explain in your own words why you believe this is true and what you can personally do in your life to never give up when it gets difficult.

_____

_____

_____

_____

Once he broke the sound barrier how fast did he accelerate to before he cut the engines? _____

Do you feel the date was significant that day? _____

What happened seven months later that changed the world for all mankind?
_____

Jesus told us to pray for the peace of Jerusalem. The city of peace was divinely connected through Jesus with our prayers. Don't be disobedient to what the Lord commanded. Stop a moment now and pray specifically for the peace of Jerusalem. Write your thoughts as the Lord speaks through you in prayer.

_____
_____
_____
_____
_____
_____
_____
_____
_____

Whether you are on the platform in worship or in your seat during corporate worship can you think of those times when it felt like a 'sound barrier' was over the worship? There was an invisible seemingly unbreakable barrier that was keeping you from breaking through? This has happened to me countless times in various places and situations. Just like Chuck Yeager we must learn to accelerate instead of pulling back our spiritual engines we are to push through even if our 'wings fall off' and we take a nosedive into the carpet in front of the throne of grace! Push through. Write in your own words what mental disciplines you can take while you are singing or playing, whether on or off the platform to help you push through and break the barrier over yourself, your family, your community, church, city, state, and even nation. What can you do? What will you do?

_____
_____
_____
_____
_____
_____
_____
_____
_____

You were created to soar with the eagles in your worship and to come up higher in His presence. Come up higher and see yourself as His finished bride image. You are to look and sound like your Bridegroom. Your image is His image. Your identity is His identity. You are not to compare yourself to anyone, ever! You are unique, adored, no one like you in all the earth because you are made like Him! There is no room for competition because there is no one to compare to you. You are His and His alone. So get over yourself and enjoy whom God made you to be! Write out some of your best qualities when you are worshiping! Go ahead; don't be afraid to tell the truth. It's humility that can truly say who you are without fear or judgment. It is not pride. Pride puffs up and is not real. You are stating truth about who you are as His worshiper. Write it out and don't hold back. You have said so many horrible things about yourself and your gifts and your instrument, now it's time to tell the truth about who you really are as His worshiper!

_____

_____

_____

_____

_____

_____

_____

_____

_____

Ephesians 2:6 states, (Look it up in your Bible, underline it, and then write it out in this workbook! If you don't have an Amplified Bible with you and you prefer that translation then use the Tones of the Throne Room book passage to copy that into this work space!)

_____

_____

_____

_____

_____

Jesus already raised us up 'higher' and has given us a seat already! Why do we settle for a lower slower position on the earth?

_____

_____

_____

_____

_____

_____

Write the verse Galatians 2:20. It's one of my favorite verses to keep me in my proper position.

_____

_____

_____

_____

The key to staying higher in the spirit is to stay hidden _____.

Let's confess together, *I am a dead person walking. I am unoffendable. I am crucified with Christ. It is no longer I who lives but Christ who lives in me."* Now say it again, and again, and again, until you believe it!

In the vision I had where I was with the Spirit of the Lord in a cemetery what was the final words the Spirit said to me?

_____

_____

_____

_____

_____

II Corinthians 10:3-6 gives us a clear picture that we may walk in the flesh we do not war in the flesh! For the weapons of our warfare are not carnal but what?

_____

_____

_____

_____

_____

Lucifer had the greatest position in the kingdom of heaven ever mentioned in the whole Bible. But in Ezekiel 28:15 we should be stopped in our pride filled tracks with one tiny little word. *"You were perfect in your ways from the day you were created, **til** iniquity was found in you."*

God's word said that Lucifer was perfect . . . TIL! We would say 'until.' This is such a tiny word that changed the course of history forever. Until iniquity, the sin of pride was found in you. As worshipers we must guard our hearts and minds against the enemy of pride, self, me, me, me! We can be perfect in all our ways, walking in our calling, anointing, and purpose, and in one moment we can be out of position and lose our position forever!

GUARD YOURSELF AGAINST PRIDE! Don't let it near you. Don't let it at the door! Keep yourself humble at the feet of Jesus! Don't allow yourself the opportunity to listen to the applause of people. Neither criticism nor applause can get a dead person off the path. Neither should either move you from your face at His feet. If people telling you bad things can move you, then when they tell you good things it can move you too. People should have no ability to get you off your God task! Obey the Spirit of God.

Worship has never been about us. Worship will always be about Him! If you can keep it that way, then you can stay in your God given position as worshiper! Pray the worshipers' prayer in the beginning of this book every day until it becomes a reality in your life of who you really are created to be! Worship is not what you do; worship is who you are!

Take a few moments as we close out this last page of this chapter and list some traps you have become aware of in your own life. List those things the enemy has used in the past to get you off track but now you recognize them and will never fall for it again. List whatever the Holy Spirit tells you to list here. If need be, take a moment to repent and move on. What we will do in private with the Father God and His Spirit usually protects us from those things becoming public later on in our lives. To me, it's worth a bit of self-examination and judging myself so I don't have to be judged in front of the whole world on judgment day!

_____
_____
_____
_____
_____
_____
_____
_____
_____
_____
_____
_____
_____
_____
_____
_____
_____
_____
_____
_____

Chapter Seven
The Wheel Within The Wheel

Chapter Seven
The Wheel Within The Wheel

In Revelation 4 we can see in those 11 verses a very descriptive image of the throne room and the worship within it. What were the four living creatures crying out day and night, never ceasing?

_____

_____

_____

In what formation were the twenty-four elders sitting?

_____

Close your eyes and imagine what this could look like and sound like in the eternal realm. Can you see the throne, and the High Priest sitting on that throne? Can you see the twenty-four elders and the four living creatures crying out in responsive worship? What were the twenty-four elders crying out in responsive worship to the four living creatures?

_____

_____

_____

Let's take a look at some of the similarities and even some of the differences between the two descriptions of the same vision. John was 'eye level' looking from a perspective of being 'caught up' higher; John was literally in the throne room at the time of his vision. Ezekiel saw it coming toward him from the north and he was still on the earth seeing into the heavenly realm of the throne room. Ezekiel was below in his view, while John was caught up higher with his view.

For John the crystal vision was the floor in front of the throne and for Ezekiel the crystal was a firmament, a ceiling above the heads of the creatures and the throne. So you see, your description of spiritual things can be different from others depending on what position you allow yourself to be in when you have an eternal experience with the Lord. Even in your worship, whether private or corporate, your view of what is happening in the realm of the eternities depends on where you are willing to 'be' during the unfolding of the vision, visitation, etc.

I don't know about you but I am not willing to stay down low and slow when Ephesians plainly states that Jesus has ALREADY seated me in heavenly places so I can have a bird's eye view! _"Come up here and I will show you what must take place after this!"_ When the angel told John to come up here and John could see into the future, that is an indication to us that if we want to see into the future of our own lives, we must be seated in heavenly places. It's very hard to see far in front of you unless you are willing to get really high to do so. If you are down on the ground and try to see way out in front of you, you can't. What's the old saying? You can't see the forest for the trees. Yep, that about sums it up in the spirit realm as well. As long as you are satisfied with the view of your present moment circumstances and situations you won't be able to see 'past' them. Your view will only be what is lower and slower down there on the ground with you.

Come up here! Says the Spirit of God to your spirit. Stop hanging around down there on the earth when you have been created to soar with the eagles!

Both prophets described the four living creatures with very similar features. List some of the similarities that you can see from reading both reports.

_____

_____

_____

_____

_____

_____

_____

_____

What is one major difference in the two men's visions of the four living creatures?

_____

_____

_____

_____

Explain how you know they were seeing the same thing but from two different perspectives.

_____

_____

_____

_____

How do you know that the 'wheel within the wheel' and the third set of wings is actually the same thing? What is the one verbal clue that makes you certain they were seeing the same thing?

_____

_____

_____

_____

What does it take from you to be able to see this type of detailed revelation from the throne room of heaven?   How can you experience these deep-detailed revelations on your own when you read and study the word of God?

_____

_____

_____

_____

_____

Look up, write out, and read aloud Joshua 1:8.

_____

_____

_____

_____

_____

Psalm 119:15, Philippians 4:8, II Timothy 2:15 all have a familiar thread running through these verses.   When you read and study your Bible you are not to run through the pages like a race, or a competition, or a type A plan to finish within a given set of days, weeks, or months.   Slow down. This is a love story, a romantic interlude of discovery with the Lover of your soul. This is the One who makes you whole.   Take your time and think about Him. Think about the layers beneath the surface 'read'.   There is so much depth below what you are seeing at first glance.

What one word or phrase do you see in these above scriptures that are mandatory to be deeper?

_____

_____

_____

_____

To know the depths of God you must experience the depths of His presence. If you stay in the shallow end of the pool of His presence you may never drown your earthly identity. It's too easy to stick your natural head up and grab an earthly breath. Come on into the deep end with me. Let His presence overwhelm you to the point you finally trust Him in your 'flesh death'.

"Precious in the sight of the Lord is the death of His saints." Psalm 116:15.

Does this scripture finally make sense to your spirit man?

My all time favorite scripture is Psalm 46:10 because it states a profound revelation. This revelation tears a huge hole in our modern day society of church thinking. It is not a 'how to do' anything in the Lord. It is not works at all but rather the exact opposite. It is a depth of trust and commitment and love that seldom one finds in an entire earths' journey into His presence.

"Be still and KNOW that He is God."

To know the revelation of who He is, one must be still. This is a discipline that most will never conquer. I will spend the rest of my life learning how to 'do' the stillness of His presence effectively. For those of us who naturally thrive on performance, perfection, people pleasing, competition, and winning, this exercise of being still to know Him takes the greatest of disciplines. If I can do it, you can do it! Discipline yourself in His presence to 'be with Him'. Don't take a list of what you need, or what you have accomplished in to the secret place with the Lover of your soul. Just go in without any 'works' coverings, and let Him see you uncovered in His presence. Let Him know how much you trust Him to be 'naked' in front of Him.

He wants us to know Him. We cannot truly know Him without 'still time' in His presence. We cannot truly know Him until we lay down our 'doing' and allow Him to mold and shape our 'being' into His own reflection and image.

The outer wheel and the inner wheel are actually _____.

How did I finally see that truth of revelation?

_____
_____
_____

As worshipers will I ever be able to lead someone where I have never been?

_____

Why is this true?

_____

How are we able to take others into the throne room of God's presence to experience the tones, frequencies, and sounds of the highest place of worship? How is it possible?

_____
_____
_____

Chapter Eight
The Four Faces

Chapter Eight
The Four Faces

Read the entire eighth chapter in the Tones of the Throne Room book before beginning this workbook chapter. As you read, do so aloud, so your brain can recall more of the facts after you finish. Singing, or saying words aloud help stimulate the frontal lobe of the brain where memory is. That's why singing nursery rhymes or the alphabet song helps you remember the lyrics many years later. After you have completed reading this lengthy chapter let's see how many questions you can answer without having to look up the answers within the pages of the book.

Who are the four living creatures?

_____

Who do they represent?

_____

What is the significance of the 'many eyes' both on the wings and the wheels?

_____

List the four faces and the direction in which they face.
   1. _____ Direction _____
   2. _____ Direction _____
   3. _____ Direction _____
   4. _____ Direction _____

Why are the four living creatures for all of eternity the closest to the throne?

_____

Why do they circle day and night and are never allowed to sit or stop moving?

_____

In Daniel 12:8-10 the scripture is exact about the instructions given to Daniel to seal up what he had seen until they will be revealed in the last days. Do you personally believe that we are in the last days? Why do you believe that?

_____

_____

_____

_____

_____

In this particular vision Jesus is described as our High Priest on His throne. What is the importance of that named position in relationship to the four living creatures being the closest to Him in that position?

_____

_____

_____

The bride of Christ will be made up of many nations and many people, including _____ and _____. The definitive indicator of who is actually His bride and who is not has to do with taking _____ and taking _____. We have two distinct groups who are 'called by His name' referenced in the scriptures. Where are those two scriptures?

_____

The Old Testament passage refers to the _____.
The New Testament passage refers to the _____.

This identity issue of taking on His name and losing our own 'self' identity, has nothing to do with a nation, but rather a _____

_____

_____.

Taking God's name as our own has much more to do with love rather than law. I can legally accept a name as my own, but unless I truly accept my 'change' of identity then I am simply going through the motions with out true trust in that name, or any enjoyment of that position given with the name. Many Christians treat the name of Jesus the same way. They accept the law of His name, but do not want the dying of self-identity that must occur in order to walk in the power, position, and authority that goes with the 'right' of that name. What would you like to say to the Lover of your soul right now and take His name to an even deeper level of heart surrender than you have ever gone before?

_____

_____

_____

_____

_____

_____

What breaks the heart of our Bridegroom Jesus Christ?

_____

_____

_____

When we think that someone else is being prideful and selfish whom should we examine more closely?

_____

Once we are confronted with the revelation of 'truth' about our own way of prideful thinking we have a choice to make. We can _____.

When I am called by His name, I have only _____.
Taking on the name of our Bridegroom causes us to become _____.

We take on His _____, _____, _____, and _____.
What is His is now ours!

All four creatures each having four distinct faces, and yet those four faces were exactly the same on each creature. So in essence then you can see that the four creatures looked exactly alike! When they moved they did not turn. Why?

_____

What was the main scripture that helped me identify the four living creatures?

_____

Because of this particular passage you can go back now if you didn't do it earlier and fill in the direction of each face!

The three tribes of Israel facing eastward in order were:
    1. _____
    2. _____
    3. _____

The three tribes of Israel facing southward in order were:
    1. _____
    2. _____
    3. _____

The three tribes of Israel facing westward in order were:
    1. _____
    2. _____
    3. _____

The three tribes of Israel facing northward in order were:
    1. _____
    2. _____
    3. _____

Each group of three tribes camped by the _____ of the leading tribe, closest to the Tent of Meeting.

Out of the twelve sons of (Jacob) who became Israel after his name change in Genesis 32, which two sons are not listed encamped around the Tent of Meeting facing east, south, west, or north?

    1. _____

    2. _____

Explain why?

_____

_____

_____

_____

The four living creatures that circle the High Priest, Jesus Christ, throne ever crying out in worship represent the _____

_____.

Why were the four leading tribes chosen for each face?

Judah was chosen because _____.

Reuben was chosen because _____.

Ephraim was chosen because _____.

Dan was chosen because _____.

Dan was the tribe that scattered over the _____.

Never give up when you are digging in the garden of God's revelation. He never hides anything from you. He hides it _____.

The insignia of our American flag is the same as the flag of _____.

Why is all this important to us as worshipers? Why does any of this matter?

_____

_____

_____

_____

_____

_____

_____

_____

_____

_____

The choice is yours. Will you come up higher and take a good look at who you really are inside of Him as you worship? Examine your heart, your motives, and your intentions. Are you still performing? Are you continuing to look for approval? Lay it all down now at His feet and never look back at who you use to be as a worshiper. You are His. You are His mirror reflected image in His face! Write down everything that the Spirit of God reveals to you that you need to finally surrender that last level of 'self' and throw yourself at His feet in pure, and holy worship!

_____
_____
_____
_____
_____
_____
_____

I dare you to look and see who you really are in His throne room. Come up higher and do more than just look this time. I want you to really see! See yourself and who you really are. See your Bridegroom and who He really is! Now worship Him. Dance for Him. Sing for Him. Shout really loud for Him. Clap your hands for Him. Whatever else the spirit of God leads you to do for Him, do it now! Lose your earthly identity, all embarrassment, all people pleasing, and just worship Him in Spirit and in Truth. He deserves it and you will love it! Go ahead and write Him a new song straight from your heart, not your head! Write it down and sing it! Write a verse or two, a chorus, and even a bridge!

_____
_____
_____
_____
_____
_____
_____
_____
_____
_____
_____
_____
_____

Remember to take out your phone and record it, so you don't forget the tune!

Chapter Nine
Eyes Within and Without

Chapter Nine
Eyes Within and Without

As we worship from a higher position our view changes. As long as we are looking from the midst of our own circumstances or situations everything still looks the same. But once we come up higher and sing a new song to the Lord our view changes! What are some things you can personally do to help you turn loose of the lower slower way of thinking and being and come up higher to experience His presence, His sounds, and His perspective?

_____
_____
_____
_____
_____
_____
_____

What can you do to put all broken places down and never pick them up again?

_____
_____
_____
_____

Use your Bible to search for a scripture in Isaiah that commands us to arise from the depression and prostration in which circumstances have kept you! Here's a hint; it's in the Amplified translation and if you start reading with Isaiah 60 and 61 you will find it! Once you find it write it out.

_____
_____
_____
_____

When a scripture starts with the verb, like, "Arise!" What is the subject of that sentence? In English it is called the understood subject and who is understood?

_____

When a sentence is structured this way it is not a suggestion but rather a command! God is commanding us, you, and me, every one who reads the verse to arise! If we don't arise then we are disobeying a direct order and command from the throne room of heaven! YOU ARISE!

This means that you cannot allow yourself to be affected by how you feel, or by others around you, or your circumstances or situations. You are only affected by the command of the Lord, which is to arise! Take the time to write out those things you have allowed to affect you. Whether it is a circumstance, a situation, a person, place, or thing, write it down and put it behind you. It's time to move forward and never look back again. Paul said in Philippians that he did one thing, to never look back. 'This one thing I do', Paul said. One thing that was the most important thing above everything else, don't look back. Can you finally for the last time lay it all down today and never ever pick it back up again? Can you stop having any identity in your broken places? If you are finally ready to have your identity totally sealed within the inside of Christ and never again to be identified with the broken places of your earth journey then take the time to write it all out! What are you leaving behind? What will you never ever look at again? What are some old identities that are being left behind?

_____

_____

_____

_____

_____

_____

_____

_____

Now that those things are settled let's move forward! Let's consider those four living creatures. Can you imagine, not have a front, two sides, left and right, and a back? Can you imagine having four fronts? It's a bit mind blowing at first to even wrap your head around the very thought of a being with four fronts, but once you do, it's amazing! That means that the four living creatures could never ever retreat or go backwards, or have a past or anything like that! That would mean that they could never get 'side tracked' as they have no sides! With only fronts then whatever direction they would be facing then they are taking forward ground at all times!

Let's discuss for a moment their wings. The Bible plainly states that they each had wings, not just wings, but 'sets of wings'. When Ezekiel saw his vision the four living creatures had _____ sets of wings. When John saw the same vision from his perspective the four living creatures had _____ sets of wings! What did Ezekiel see that was totally different from John?

_____

_____

_____

_____

John described a set of wings to be very similar to the wheel within the wheel that Ezekiel saw. Write out the description and in your opinion after reading the entire chapter what (or who) could all those eyes represent?

_____

_____

_____

_____

_____

This could be a real number of 12,000 people from each tribe of Israel or it could be a figurative number representing the divine government of God brought from heaven to earth by the number '12'. Whether it is literal or figurative there is no doubt this is a representation of the redeemed bride of Christ from within the chosen people of Israel. These four living creatures will circle the throne of God crying out for all of eternity . . .

_____

_____

Then the twenty-four elders will respond in worship crying toward the throne,

_____

_____

Why do the four living creatures revolve around the throne forever and ever, never sitting and never stopping the movement of circular motion?

_____

—

Are you just a little bit envious of their position and the fact that for all eternity they get to worship the King? Don't concern yourself with that! You can worship the King for all eternity too! Stop before you move on to the next chapter and worship Him right now. Tell Him who He really is in your personal and private life. Try to tell Him who He is without telling what He has done for you! Just proclaim His goodness and His character! What a great spiritual exercise to lift Him up and magnify His holy name! Write it down after you finish if you would like to do so.

_____

_____

_____

_____

_____

_____

_____

Chapter Ten
The Twenty-Four Elders

Chapter Ten
The Twenty-Four Elders

Just as Ezekiel saw a wheel within a wheel, so did John. The difference was in perspective. John's vision showed the four living creatures circling the throne of the High Priest as Jesus Christ crying out in complete and forever worship. This portion of John's vision represented the inner circle of the wheel within a wheel. Then John saw the twenty-four elders in circular position in the outer realm of the vision of the throne room. These twenty-four elders are forever crying out in responsive worship to the four living creatures in constant sounding worship to the great High Priest Jesus Christ. They are seated, not moving, until they are so moved in their worship that they fall down on their knees, casting their crowns at the feet of Jesus! This motion from the twenty-four elders is a significant sign of whom they represent.

First, they are seated. In the verse Ephesians 2:6 we see a great description as to where we are seated once we receive Jesus Christ as our Lord and Savior. It is not when we 'get to heaven' that we are seated in heavenly places but when we are born again that we are seated in heavenly places! So while my feet are still held on this earth in 'time' my spirit and soul are seated in heavenly places with Christ Jesus. So right this moment as you are reading in the Tones book and working this page in the workbook, where are you? Are you stuck in earth's time line of thinking or are you sitting in your God given rightful position in heavenly places? Write out your position at this moment and explain why you feel you are in this place. If you are not in your rightful position take the necessary steps now to get your mind in position and take your place!

_____
_____
_____
_____
_____
_____
_____
_____

In the ancient Hebrew numbers, the number twenty-four represents what and whom?

_____
_____
_____
_____
_____

In two different passages of scripture we are given proof of our position once we have received Jesus Christ as our Lord and Savior.   Write out these two passages.

Revelation 1:6

_____
_____
_____
_____
_____

Revelation 5:10

_____
_____
_____
_____
_____

Simply by the understanding of these two verses of scripture one can easily see the position set aside for all mankind through the shed blood of Jesus Christ. What are those two positions?

_____

Did you earn your way into either of these positions?

_____

Who made you kings and priests?

_____

You are a king and a priest unto _____.

By understanding the positions given to us through the blood of Jesus Christ then why do you suppose many never walk in or sit upon the seat given to them already?

_____
_____
_____
_____

What has kept you out of position until now? _____

_____
_____
_____

Do you see who you really are? Who are you?

_____

_____

_____

Heaven expects those of the priesthood to live at a . . .

_____

_____

_____

When conversations are tainted with unholy and infectious words and actions are screaming 'no accountability' what behavior is being revealed?

_____

_____

In general people want to live like the world and yet be . . .

_____

God knows the _____ and intents of the _____.

We who say we are worshipers of God will be _____.

When you worship God what sounds are coming forth from your instrument?

_____

_____

_____

Are there still sounds of 'self, flesh, pain, hurt, and broken places'? If so, take a moment to repent of those sounds and ask the Holy Spirit to fill you with His sounds and His light! Come on, be real, and honest; just talk to Him. He knows you far better than you know yourself.

_____

_____

_____

_____

So the four living creatures represent the redeemed Jewish bride of Christ from the twelve tribes of Israel. Who then are the twenty-four elders representing using Acts 15 as your guide to discovery?

_____

_____

_____

These twenty-four elders sitting on the thrones are much more than the _____.
They represent . . .

_____
_____
_____
_____

In Psalm 72 there are twenty-four positional phrases that define and outline the priesthood positions. List them here please.

1. _____
2. _____
3. _____
4. _____
5. _____
6. _____
7. _____
8. _____
9. _____
10. _____
11. _____
12. _____
13. _____
14. _____
15. _____
16. _____
17. _____
18. _____
19. _____
20. _____
21. _____
22. _____
23. _____
24. _____

In this Psalm we see what Jesus did, is doing, and will continue to do as our High Priest. Christ is our _____ according to the book of Hebrews.

It takes the love of God for us, then our responsive love choice back to Him, to bring about our new birth (new beginnings) experience to allow us the priesthood position for all of eternity.   16 (love) + 8 (new creation, new beginning) = 24 (priesthood position forever and ever in worship)

I see King Jesus high and lifted up on the highest of all high thrones in the center of our worship! I see all kinds of artistic expressions of worship going forth; four living creatures dancing around the throne, colors of emerald circling the throne as the Spirit of God coincides with the spirits of redeemed mankind painting gorgeous colorful, bright and filled with light artist's renderings in worship. I see redeemed kings and priests falling on their faces in worship, crying out in responsive glorious sounds, and casting their crowns at His feet in total surrender in worship! Can you see it? Close your eyes and imagine with your spirit the throne room experience. Can you see yourself right there in the midst of it all? What are you doing? What are you saying, proclaiming, and singing? Write down what you see and hear!

_____
_____
_____
_____
_____
_____
_____
_____

Do you see a 'flat' vision becoming vertical in His presence? The circle is more than just a circle within a circle! It is a vertical ever-rising spiral staircase of thrones, tones, sounds of worship ever rising higher and higher around the great High Priest's throne! There you are! I see you! You are dancing, worshiping, singing, shouting, and crying out! Can you see me? I see you!! Write what you see now!

_____
_____
_____
_____
_____
_____
_____

Each throne as a tone, a specific sound, frequency, movement, color all its individual unique and personal worship sound! That's you! You are different on purpose. You were not created a copy. You are unique, ON PURPOSE! Own and enjoy your difference right now. Write out how you feel you are different in your worship than everyone else, and not in a negative way, but in a positive ownership way of your precious difference!

_____
_____
_____
_____

Chapter Eleven
If We Keep Silent

Chapter Eleven
If We Keep Silent

Luke 11:2, "So He said to them, "When you pray, say, Our Father in heaven, Hallowed by Your name. Your kingdom come. Your will be done on earth as it is in heaven."

For years I said this prayer by memory but one day while meditating on this particular passage of scripture I saw three amazing revelations that I had never 'seen' before.   I use the quotes, as there are times we look at something literally every day and not see it.   Here is a perfect example of the difference in 'seeing something' and having a 'revelation' of something.

First I noticed that Jesus specifically told them to speak aloud when they pray. He said, "When you pray, SAY!"   Don't waste your time praying without using the supernatural creative power and authority I have given to the earth through the sound waves of the spoken word!   When you pray, make sure you SAY!

Then two more successive revelations came right off the page at me.   Now that you are saying aloud when you are speaking to the Father, (notice Jesus taught the disciples to pray to the Father! Our Father!)   Once you are praying correctly, that is aloud, and you are praying to the correct Godhead position, Father, then make sure you do these two things.   Use your creative sound to call the kingdom of heaven to the earth.   Your kingdom, 'COME!'   Your will, 'DONE!'   Call the realm of heaven to earth.   You come up higher, and the kingdom of heaven will meet you in the earth realm!   Then make a declaration of the will of God, finished, completed, and done!

In the last chapter of Revelation Jesus said three times, that He is coming. He is coming. He is coming.   Each time He speaks about His coming there are other instructions but the last time He says that He is coming the voicing changes to the voice of the bride led by the Spirit of God, and we respond, "Even so, COME LORD JESUS!"   This is responsive worship praying.   And it is obedience to what Jesus taught the disciples and thus us also, to complete the finished work of obedient prayer.   Your kingdom, "Come!"   Your will, "Done!"   Do you see the correlation between the teaching of Jesus in Luke 11 and the final words spoken by Jesus, our Bridegroom in the last few verses of the book of Revelation? Explain what these two revelations mean to you personally and how will your daily prayers change?

_____

_____

_____

_____

Don't just think in your mind when you pray. Say your prayers out loud to stimulate the cognitive particles of your brain! This will help your mind to grasp what is _____. This brings your _____ in line with God's Word. Making sound changes our _____. Making sound helps us remember what we are _____ and it stimulates the _____ where our memories are stored.

We respond to music and the sound frequencies of music on a purely _____. This stimulates our brain and causes our brain waves to respond to, and get into rhythm and harmony with whatever sounds we allow our person to hear. What you allow into your being does truly affect what comes out of your being! Out of the abundance of the heart the mouth SPEAKS! Your mouth makes sound in direct proportion to the sound that has been received into the heart.

God in heaven likes to be acknowledged as our _____. It's not enough for us to know who He is. We need to express who He is with sound waves in words back to Him! This is pure and holy worship! Stop a moment and tell Father God who He really is to you!

_____

_____

_____

When we first receive a revelation from God, why does it feel like it comes so fast and then we can't seem to recall it later?

_____

How can we slow it down enough to retain it and receive it fully?

_____

_____

What moves faster, light or sound? _____
Heaven moves at the speed of _____.
Earth moves at the speed of _____.

We receive most things one dimensionally, and yet the revelations of Heaven through dreams, visions, and most importantly through His word are given to us in 3D. How can we get our flat horizontal brain receptors to see more clearly the way God sees and gives His revelations?

_____

_____

In the vision that I saw of worship in the throne room of heaven list what was praising God. Try not to miss anything; list as many as you can see in my paragraphs. Then close your eyes and you look into the throne room. Imagine through my descriptions what worship looks and sounds like within the 'tones of the throne room' and then look deeper. What else can you see that must be worshiping? Nothing can be silent in the throne room of God. What else is there that must be sounding praise and worship back to Him?

_____

_____

_____

_____

_____

_____

_____

Each throne becomes a tone. I can imagine the throne room of God evolving right in front of my vision eyes and literally everything begins to worship Him! The thrones begin to spiral upward like a worshiping sound wave of worship and praise! The thrones become the steps on the staircase (at least 3 stories high according to Ezekiel!). Higher, higher, higher the stairway of praise begins to rise until neither end is visible. This is an infinite stairway of praise from glory to glory! Each step becomes a 'key of the kingdom'.

Matthew 16:19, Jesus said, "And I will give you the keys of the kingdom . . . "

Jesus said 'keys of' not 'keys to' the kingdom. If the keys in reference here were what we imagine an actual locking and unlocking key then Jesus would have used the preposition 'keys to' the kingdom. But Jesus did not use that phrase! He used, 'I will give you the keys of the kingdom.'

First of all, there is only one kingdom so if He was talking about an actual key to unlock and lock the kingdom of heaven, He would have surely used the phrase 'key to'. He would not have used the plural of the word keys and He most certainly would have used the preposition 'to' not 'of'. So with this tiny little word change it seems everything shifts into place of true revelation.

The only time anyone would use the preposition 'of' with the word 'keys' would be in reference to the language of music. Let's do that song in the 'key of'. And of course there are 7 different keys in the music language when in reference to sound waves, frequencies, pitches, etc. These keys are A, B, C, D, E, F, and G. Once you get to G, then next one is a repeat at a higher pitch. We begin again with A. Seven tones in the musical language and it brings us full circle back to the beginning at a higher or lower level depending on whether ascending or descending the scale. You know this without even realizing it if you are not a musician from the musical "The Sound of Music". 'Do' a deer, a female deer. 'Re' a drop of golden sun. 'Mi' a name I call myself. 'Fa' a long long way to run. 'Sol' a needle pulling thread. 'La' a note that follows 'Sol'. 'Ti', a drink with jam and bread, and that brings us back to 'Do'. You know the lyrics. Seven movements of tone, frequency, and pitch and the circle is complete. Of course the music language is completed with God's perfect number of movements.

In Revelation 4 we read, "Seven lamps of fire were burning before the throne, which are the seven Spirits of God." I don't believe in coincidence. I believe the seven Spirits of God are in direct relationship to the seven whole tones of musical sound we have here in a musical language on the earth. Lucifer was thrown to the earth after he fell as the anointed cherub of worship, and I believe those seven tones of the musical language we now use to worship in the throne room as the very sounds of the Seven Spirits of God. Each tone brings a different feeling, a different portal into the realm of heaven. Each tone brings another level of heaven to earth. Then why are we silent when we should be making sound? Answer that personally please. Why are you silent when you should be making sound?

_____

_____

_____

_____

_____

_____

_____

The numerical value of twenty-four is not the point really. Twenty-four thrones represent an ascending sound into the heavenlies within the throne room. Twenty-four is the number for priesthood; the sounds of the priesthood fill with the throne room of God! It is not a concrete amount, rather than a positional definition of who will be allowed to make responsive worship within the throne room.

Look up and write out I Peter 2:9.

_____

_____

_____

_____

After writing out this scripture and seeing the understood subject 'you', list below all the attributes of which heaven says that you are!

1. _____
2. _____
3. _____
4. _____
5. _____

God has 'called' you. Then why have you not come when He called? You are called by God! He has called you. What is keeping you even now from answering the call and walking in the divine will and purpose of God for you? Be honest. Now admit it and quit it. It's time to move forward!

_____
_____
_____
_____
_____
_____
_____
_____
_____

_____

In the book of Esther she had been inside the kingdom of nine years by the time she was confronted with a choice that would change everything for herself and for her nation. What did her choice come down to for her? She had to what?

_____
_____
_____
_____
_____

When confronted with a God command in her life if she did not obey what would it cost her and her entire family?

_____
_____
_____
_____

There is a time when your silence is still permitted without cost but that time has passed for all of us. We are confronted daily now to make sound for His glory. What will you do differently in your daily life, your work place, your neighborhood, your family and friends? Write it down and make a commitment to the Lord right here. This is a type of vow, commitment, even a legal contract of statement between you and your Father God now. What will you do from now on for His glory?

_____
_____
_____
_____
_____
_____
_____

In America we are confronted with a false god sound because of our decades of silence and complacency. Because we have allowed other gods in our land, with our silent consent, we now must face the consequences of those actions. There is no magic fairy dust to make it all go away now. We cannot reverse the clock and go back three or four decades to change what we have allowed through laws, governmental politics, and yes, even the silence of the church. But we can change the future for our personal walk, our personal lives, family, and community. We can do it with our divine sound waves of worship. We can bring down strongholds because we are a chosen people, given a sound of worship that can break the stronghold over this nation. Write out by the Spirit of God a song of declaration for this nation and land. Pray in the Holy Ghost for a few minutes then interpret what the Spirit is saying to the earth. Make it a melody of war, and sing it loudly in the throne room of God.

_____
_____
_____
_____
_____
_____
_____
_____
_____
_____

Find your voice and use it for God's glory. WE WILL NOT KEEP SILENT! WE WILL NOT KEEP SILENT! WE WILL NOT KEEP SILENT! Say it with me. Make it personal. I WILL NOT KEEP SILENT! I WILL NOT KEEP SILENT! I WILL NOT KEEP SILENT! Now pray in tongues in the spirit for a while. Take your time alone in the throne room of God. Find your own personal 'tone of the throne room'. There is a sound a frequency within your instrument that the Spirit of God wants to make through you now. Don't be afraid. No one is listening to you. You are alone. You are God's instrument. Allow Him to play you now. Once you have finished, write down what you can remember that He is saying through you.

_____
_____
_____
_____
_____
_____
_____
_____
_____
_____
_____
_____
_____
_____
_____
_____
_____
_____
_____
_____
_____
_____
_____
_____
_____

WE WILL NOT KEEP SILENT! I WILL NOT KEEP SILENT! I AM A PRIEST AND I HAVE A 'THRONE TONE' TO USE FOR ETERNITY FOR HIS GLORY! I'M STARTING NOW WHILE HERE ON EARTH. I CALL HEAVEN TO THE EARTH. YOUR KINGDOM, 'COME!' YOUR WILL, 'DONE!'

Chapter Twelve
Tones of the Throne Room

Chapter Twelve
Tones of the Throne Room

Ezekiel 41:6-7, "The side chambers were in three stories, one above the other, thirty chambers in each story; they rested on ledges which were for the side chambers all around, that they might be supported, but not fastened to the wall of the temple. As one went up from story to story, the side chambers became wider all around . . ."

When I wrote Tones of the Throne Room I knew the Throne of God, inner sanctuary, Holy of Holies within the realm of heaven, was a spiral staircase of sound, ascending higher and higher. I knew it! I knew it by the spirit and by much meditation and revelation.   I have read the book of Ezekiel every year since 2000, but for whatever reason my intellect had never grasped the three stories high revelation written about by Ezekiel of what he saw in a vision of the inner chamber of the temple.   I saw it also! I saw it in a vision but when I wrote the Tones of the Throne Room book I had not put all these pieces together!   Here is the scripture in chapter 41 (and chapter 42 mentions three stories also) to prove what I know by the spirit and truth revelation.

After reading the entire chapter twelve, the final chapter in Tones of the Throne Room, I want you to slow down a bit more and spend more time in 'Selah' (pause and calmly think on that).   If you miss the depth of the tones message you may not tap into the deeper sound of your own throne room.   For you are the temple of the Holy Ghost, and the Tones of the Throne Room are within you!

I Corinthians 6:19, "Or do you not know that your body is the temple of the Holy Spirit who is in you, whom you have from God, and you are not your own?"

This is not the first time we read such an awesome revelation in God's word. Just look at *I Corinthians 3:16-17, "Do you not know that you are the temple of God and that the Spirit of God dwells in you? If anyone defiles the temple of God, God will destroy him. For the temple of God is holy, which temple you are."*

Go ahead and say this aloud so your own ears can hear you say this!   *Faith comes by hearing and hearing by the word of God! (Romans 10:17)*

I AM THE TEMPLE OF THE HOLY GHOST.
I AM THE TEMPLE OF THE HOLY GHOST.
I AM THE TEMPLE OF THE HOLY GHOST.

You may need to repeat a few more times to get the truth inside you. You are the temple of the Holy Ghost! Do you not know this by now? We will discuss your identity in Christ as a worshiper and as His temple in my next book on worship. But suffice it to say if you do not know who you really are as a worshiper of the Most High God, you will never be able to fulfill your God given destiny to the highest and best levels!

What words, phrases, or statements have been said to you, about you, etc. that are still playing in the memories of your mind today? Let's settle and seal those negative statements that are not truth of who you really are. Let's write them out on the next page, and then put a huge big X over all of them, with the word NOT written across the X! God says you are His worshiper. God says you are His temple. God says you should know this! It's time to own this identity of who you really are inside of Christ and Christ inside of you! Come on, dig deeper into your brain of memory and write out every negative thing ever said to you, over you, and about you.

As you write it out, dump it and the power of it right out of your mind and brain!

_____
_____
_____
_____
_____
_____
_____
_____
_____
_____
_____
_____

Don't leave out one thing. Write it all out and dump it! Now put a huge X over the entire list of statements and then write a huge NOT across the X. Now flush the negative non-God statements right out of your consciousness forever. Let's fill your memory up now with whom God says you really are.

I am a worshiper of the Most High God.
I belong to God. He bought me with the price of His only Son's blood.
I am covered in the blood of Jesus Christ.
I am the temple of the Holy Ghost.
I am clean, pure, and holy before God.
I am a priest and a king because of Jesus Christ.
I am a child of God.

I am a joint heir with Jesus Christ.

Now you write out a few more statements of who you really are! Come on; be truthful, only say what God says about you in His word.

_____

_____

_____

_____

_____

_____

_____

_____

_____

_____

_____

When I first received the revelation of the wheel within the wheel of the throne room of God, making the inner circle the four living creatures, and the outer circle being the twenty-four elders, how many ways did I break down the circles? How did I see it first, and then second and finally the full vertical revelation?

_____

_____

_____

_____

_____

The Spirit of God said to me, "_____."

Once I saw the truth of the vertical revelation I saw that the twenty-four positional thrones were _____ of frequency and the twenty-four tones were _____.

Lucifer was described as having his internal parts made up of frequencies and musical pitches. His insides were musical instruments for giving worship in the throne room. He fell. God made you and me, and put pitches, tones, and frequencies inside our very DNA, our cellular system has a sound wave in the very core of every human cell! We are made of frequencies, and pitches within us for giving worship! We replaced Lucifer as the highest worshiper in the throne room, but instead of one being God made an entire human race of people, once redeemed, and in their God given place, of kings and priests, we can utilize our inner beings in constant and forever worship for our King!

When we align the tones, we must tap into the musical language of seven named tones. Do-Re-Mi-Fa-Sol-La-Ti. When you assign the musical scale in a circular motion of movement, like a three story spiral staircase, one must make _____ circles of _____ and a _____ to complete the twenty-four positions within the throne room.

When disorder is met and synchronized, then order is brought by harmony. Write out the scripture for Matthew 18:18-19, using the Amplified translation (if you don't have one, use your phone to look it up on Bible Gateway.

_____
_____
_____
_____
_____
_____
_____
_____

Notice the Bible talks about harmonizing and making a symphony. These are musical terms for the power of agreement. (You can study more about this in our book, Two Becoming One.) As a race of human beings we are created to harmonize on a purely cellular level. When our cells get into disharmony, then we deal with anxiety, stress, sickness, disease, and other issues. We were created as a race of people to walk in harmony from the very depths of our cellular level to the highest levels of our consciousness.

When 'Do' is the 1st throne (tone), and 'Re' is the 2nd throne (tone), and 'Mi' is the 3rd throne (tone), each toned position has meaning of intercession, through worship and praise. List the definitions given for the Hebrew meanings of each toned number.

1st _____
2nd _____
3rd _____
4th _____
5th _____
6th _____
7th _____
8th _____
9th _____
10th _____
11th _____
12th _____
13th _____
14th _____

15th _____
16th _____
17th _____
18th _____
19th _____
20th _____
21st _____
22nd _____
23rd _____
24th _____

These twenty-four positions have meaning.   Each throne/tone is perfectly set in position for intercession, worship, and praise.   The frequencies, and sounds make a defined and purposeful intercessory request, or testimony within the realm of the throne room of God.

When we sing the scriptures we are releasing the _____
_____
_____

The tones lined up tell the story of _____.

When the toned frequencies for all the 'Do' positions are lined up from within the throne room they tell the story of redemption that says
_____

Put the stories of redemption in your own words for each position.

All the 'Re' positions say
_____

The 'Mi' positions say
_____

The 'Fa' positions say
_____

The 'Sol' positions say
_____

The 'La' positions say
_____

The 'Ti' positions say

_____

How amazing is the intricacies of our God? He is so awesome!

When we walk in unity, which in ancient Hebrew means to strongly fence the door, and leave no options of exit,

_____
_____
_____
_____

Humanity cannot survive on its own. Humanity without God . . .

_____.

Revelation 3:20 states, "Behold, I stand at the door and knock; if anyone hears My voice and opens the door, I will come in . . ."

There are two actions required for us to have the scripture above fulfilled in our lives. We must first _____ His voice, and then we must _____ Then He promises He will come in!

The grace of God creates divine order and God's

_____
_____

Mankind left without God always falls into rebellion and depravity but with God we

_____

In your own words tell how the last chapter of the book of Revelation and the last story told around the throne in worship is the best of all the stories.   Read the chapter in Revelation aloud first, then the definition of the 'Ti' tones. Then write a song to the Lord using these definitions to love on the Lover of your soul.

_____
_____
_____
_____
_____
_____
_____
_____
_____

You are the tone of His glory! You cry out forever who He really is! This in turn will also solidify who you really are! Get ready to worship higher than you have ever worshiped before! You are the temple of the Holy Ghost! You are filled with His tones and His sound! Don't be afraid or concerned with how you think you sound! You are sounding just like you were created to sound! Don't hold back, or be intimidated! You are His glorious instrument created for His glory! You are the tone of His throne room that was engraved within your cellular level from before you were born, even in your mother's womb! Write out your last love song to His throne. Make sure you write one verse of who you are because of His hand upon you. Then a verse should be designated to who He is in your life now! Go ahead! It's awesome to worship Him from your own toned position!

_____
_____
_____
_____
_____
_____
_____
_____
_____
_____
_____
_____
_____
_____
_____
_____
_____
_____

Prayer of Salvation

If you have never made Jesus the Lord of your life, or if you would like to re-dedicate your life to Him, please pray this prayer of salvation.

Heavenly Father, I come to You admitting that I am a sinner. Right now, I choose to turn away from sin and I ask You to cleanse me of all unrighteousness. I believe that Your Son, Jesus, died on the cross to take away my sins. I also believe that He rose again from the dead so that I might be forgiven of my sins and be made righteous through faith in Him. I call upon the name of Jesus Christ to be the Lord and Savior of my life. Jesus, I choose to follow You and I ask that You fill me with the power of the Holy Spirit. I declare right now that I am a child of God! I am free from sin and full of the righteousness of God. I am saved, in Jesus' name. Amen.

Please contact us to let us know you prayed this prayer!

About the Author

Cheryl Salem walked the runway to become Miss America 1980, despite what appeared to be all odds stacked against her. A horrific car crash resulting in a physical handicap and over 100 stitches in her face, were no match for what God had planned for her life. Through childlike faith in Him, she overcame the obstacles and eventually took the crown in Atlantic City! She has used this distinction as a springboard to launch the Gospel into churches, conferences, and many television appearances. According to Cheryl, "None of these things would be possible, if not for my Jesus."

In 1985, Cheryl married the love of her life, Harry Salem II. Harry and Cheryl Salem travel the world ministering the gospel, telling people that Jesus loves them and that He is returning soon! Their lives revolve around seeking the Lord and where He would have them go. Two by two they travel, loving God's people, living and moving in His anointing.

In 1999, Harry and Cheryl endured the loss of their 6-year-old daughter, Gabrielle. As they boldly took steps of faith to overcome the agonizing pain of Gabrielle's death, they ask God to restore them and for souls to come into His kingdom. God has restored the Salem family and because of His mighty anointing, the altars have been full!

Harry and Cheryl are committed to leading godly lives as an example to others. Roman has married a beautiful young lady, Stephanie, and she has become their daughter-in-love. Healing and restoration has come full circle to the Salem family with the miracle birth of Roman and Stephanie's daughter, Mia Gabrielle and son, Roman Jr.

Harry Salem III continues in the family ministry as he has done since he was a child. He has completed his doctorate in Theology, while Roman and Stephanie are ministering as a couple to both youth and adult services across the country. Harry III, Roman and Stephanie minister with Harry and Cheryl in the Salem Family Ministries events.

Together, Harry and Cheryl have written over 30 books and produced numerous music and ministry CDs to help enable believers to not only overcome but to excel in their Christian lives.

They love people and they love pouring themselves out because God's immense mercy, grace, and love keep them filled up in return.

The Spirit of God is flowing through Cheryl in an amazing way as He leads her to minister in a prophetic manner that involves a flow of music and teaching that is sung, instead of spoken. After surviving and overcoming cancer twice over the last 14 years, she believes that her call to rebuild and restore worship God's way is the mantle she will fulfill throughout the rest of her life.

Cheryl is a worshiper above all else. She ministers to ladies events across the country, encouraging women to reach their godly potential, but her main objective and central focus for Salem Family Ministries is to take Harry and Cheryl's unique, tag-team style of ministry into churches and gatherings all over this world, going out two by two, to reach families one by one for God's glory! (Luke 10:1-2)

Cheryl Salem

Books by Harry and Cheryl Salem

I Am A Worshiper

Age of Mystery

The Sound of the Spirit

Tones of the Throne Room

Rebuilding the Ruins of Worship Workbook

Rebuilding the Ruins of Worship

We Who Worship Workbook

We Who Worship

The Rise of an Orphan Generation: Longing for a Father

The Presence of Angels in Your Life

Don't Kill Each Other! Let God Do It!

Entering Rest – Be Still – A 40-Day Journey into the Presence of God

Obtaining Peace – A 40-Day Prayer Journal

2 Becoming 1

The Choice is Yours

Overcoming Fear – A 40-Day Prayer Journal

Every Body Needs Balance

From Grief to Glory

From Mourning to Morning

Distractions from Destiny

Speak the Word Over Your Family for Finances

Speak the Word Over Your Family for Healing

Speak the Word Over Your Family for Salvation

*Fight in the Heavenlies**

*It's Too Soon to Give Up**

Being #1 at Being #2

*An Angel's Touch**

For Men Only

A Royal Child

The Mommy Book

*How to Get a Balanced Body**

*Simple Facts; Salvation, Healing & the Holy Ghost**

*Health & Beauty Secrets**

*Choose to be Happy**

Abuse ... Bruised but not Broken

You Are Somebody

A Bright Shining Place - The Story of a Miracle

*Check for availability

We would love to hear from you.   There are many ways to stay connected with us. You can receive our newsletter by giving us your email address through our web site. It's free and easy.

Salem Family Ministries
P. O. Box 1595
Cathedral City, CA 92234
www.salemfamilyministries.org

Like our page on Facebook
Salem Family Ministries

Subscribe to our YouTube channel
Salem Family Ministries

Connect through my Twitter or Periscope account
Cheryl Salem @cherylsalem1980

Made in the USA
Las Vegas, NV
27 August 2022